INSIDE YOUR AMAZING SPIDER-MAN ANNUAL...

CAN YOU SPOT THE EIGHT RED
AND BLUE SPIDER SYMBOLS HIDDEN
INSIDE THIS ANNUAL?

£6.99

D0586370

HOW I BECAME SPIDEY...

By Peter Parker

"Hey, gang! Ever wondered how I came to be the amazing Spider-Man with an even more amazing personality!? Well, read on and I'll tell you everything you need to know..."

1 HOME SWEET HOME

After the death of my parents I was taken in by my Uncle Ben and Aunt May. They taught me right from wrong and raised me like a son, and I'll always be grateful to them.

2 SCHOOL'S OUT

Even though I loved learning at school (especially science), I was completely hopeless at sports. Unfortunately, this led to me picking up the nickname 'Puny Parker'!

3

Whilst at a science exhibition, I was bitten on the hand by a spider that had been exposed to radiation. I immediately fell ill, but when I awoke, I discovered I had gained amazing spider-like powers!

WEIRD SCIENCE

AMAZING ANIMAL ABILITIES

I always wonder what powers I would have gained if I was bitten by another radioactive animal. Instead of the amazing Spider-Man, I could have been the amazing... Duck-Billed-Platypus-Man!

I've made up a list of new Super Heroes below. Can you guess each one's possible powers opposite?

NEW HEROES

BRILLIANT BED BUG-MAN

INCREDIBLE CRAB-MAN

OUTSTANDING OCTOPUS-MAN

SENSATIONAL SKUNK-MAN

MAGNIFICENT MOLE-MAN

4 SHOWBIZ SPIDEY

With my newfound powers, I tried to get into show business. I designed a snazzy costume and some web-shooters and started to perform my 'Spider-Man' act!

If you had to design a Super Hero costume, what would it look like? Give it a go!

5 TRAGEDY STRIKES

When leaving a gig, a thief ran past me followed by a security guard. With my powers, I could have easily stopped him, but I figured it wasn't my problem...

However, later that night, my Uncle Ben was murdered by the same thief!

POSSIBLE POWERS

Ability to dig really big holes in double-quick time to trap thieves escaping on foot!

Can sucker punch up to eight super villains at any one time!

A villain's worst nightmare — he has the ability to catch crooks while they sleep!

Can inflict an extremely painful pinch, which causes felons to surrender!

Can create a super powerful stench, which causes criminals to fall unconscious!

ANSWERS ON PAGE 62!

6 A HERO IS BORN

FROM THAT MOMENT ON, I KNEW I HAD BEEN GIVEN MY POWERS FOR A REASON. WITH GREAT POWER COMES GREAT RESPONSIBILITY, AND I WOULD ALWAYS USE MY GIFT TO PROTECT THE INNOCENT AND MAINTAIN JUSTICE!

SPIDEY SKILLS!

WHEN A RADIOACTIVE SPIDER BIT PETER PARKER IT CREATED ONE OF THE GREATEST SUPER HEROES THE WORLD HAS EVER SEEN! HOW? BY GRANTING HIM AMAZING ARACHNID-LIKE ABILITIES OF COURSE!

WALL-CRAWLING

Spidey can stick to almost any surface, which allows him to climb walls, cling to ceilings, and more importantly, hang on to criminals!

WEB-SLINGING

Parker used his scientific know-how to invent a special web-fluid and web-shooters. Thanks to his incredible arachnid agility and cool gadgets, Spidey can web-sling all over the city in double-quick time, ensnare his enemies, and create web-like shapes to save innocent citizens.

SPIDER STRENGTH

Having proportionate strength to that of a human-sized spider means Spidey can mix it up with the toughest villains around. He can lift a whopping 10 tonnes, but has been known to lift twice as much when his life depends on it!

SPIDER-SENSE

Perhaps Spidey's greatest power is his spider-sense, which is like an early warning device that alerts him to all dangers. This means the wall-crawler can avoid almost any danger if he relies on his instincts!

SPEED AND AGILITY

Spidey has superhuman speed and amazing agility! He is roughly 15 times more agile than a regular human, so while he isn't as strong as some Super Heroes, he is certainly faster!

BITTEN BY AN IRRADIATED SPIDER, WHICH GRANTED HIM INCREDIBLE ABILITIES, **PETER PARKER** LEARNED THE ALL-IMPORTANT LESSON, THAT WITH GREAT POWER THERE MUST ALSO COME GREAT RESPONSIBILITY. AND SO HE BECAME--

--THE AMAZING SPIDER-MAN

What's this? Spider-Man terrorizing a serene neighborhood with the help of *Doctor Octopus'* tentacles?

This can't be right...*can it?*

Read on, friend, and find out...

HOW SPIDER-MAN LEARNED TO STOP WORRYING AND LOVE THE ARMS!

ZEB WELLS
WRITER

PATRICK SCHERBERGER
PENCILS

NORMAN LEE
INKS

GURU eFX
COLORS

AMANDA CONNER and SOTOMAYOR
COVER

DAVE SHARPE
LETTERER

BRAD JOHANSEN
PRODUCTION

NATHAN COSBY
ASST. EDITOR

MACKENZIE CADENHEAD with MARK PANICCIA
EDITORS

JOE QUESADA
CHIEF

DAN BUCKLEY
PUBLISHER

7

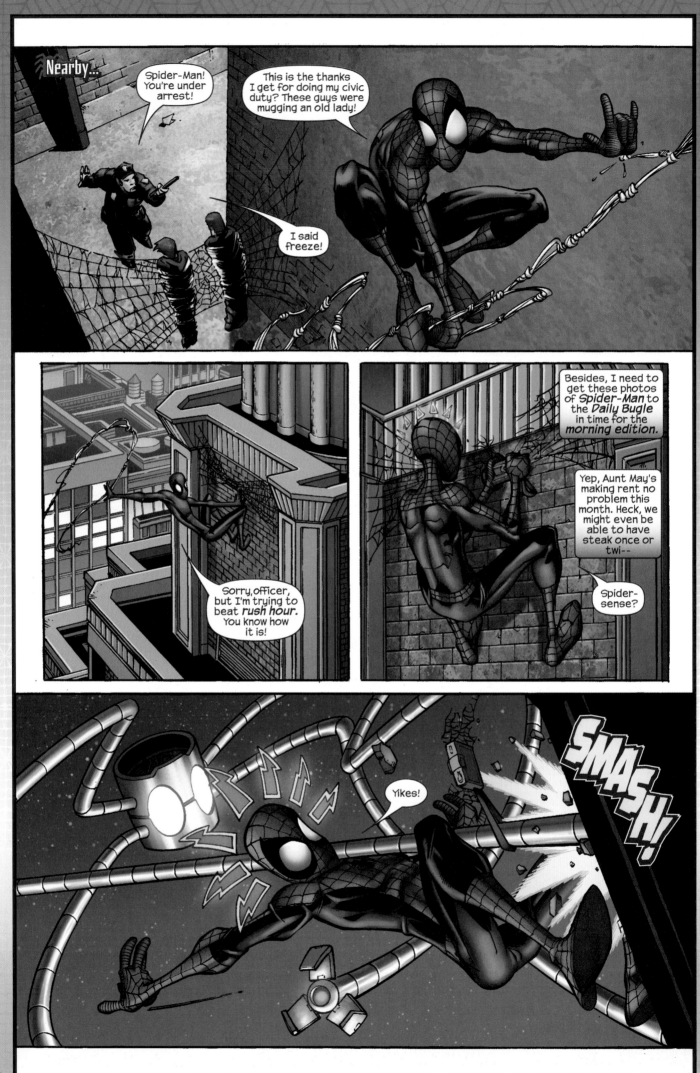

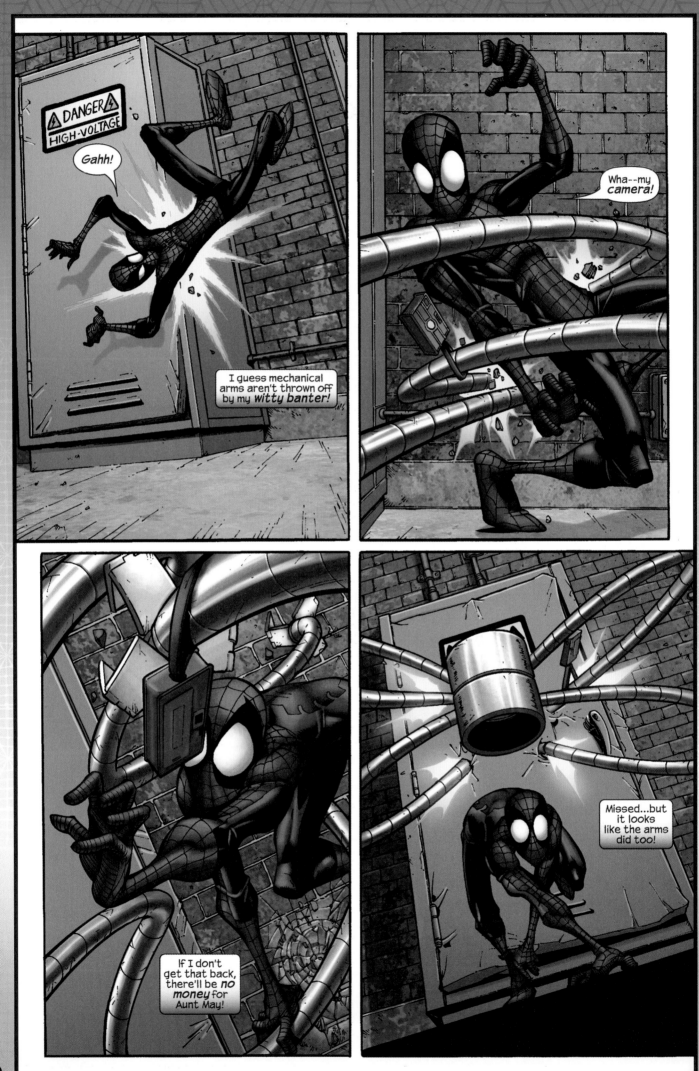

CONTINUED ON PAGE 16...

13

MEET ONE OF SPIDER-MAN'S TOUGHEST RIVALS, THE DEADLY...

DOCTOR OCTOPUS

Otto Octavius' tough upbringing led him to become a shy and withdrawn child.

Throwing himself into his education, he became a science *whiz kid* and grew up to be a respected nuclear physicist and inventor.

He built a set of advanced *mechanical arms*, which were not affected by radiation and could perform precise movements, to help him with his research into atomic physics.

CRIMINAL FILE #997455

PERSONAL DETAILS

Real name: Otto Octavius
Height: 5'9"
Weight: 17.5 Stone
Hometown: Schenectady, NY.
Occupation: Criminal mastermind, former atomic researcher.

SKILLS AND ABILITIES

Doctor Octopus is extremely intelligent and is the leading expert on all things nuclear. He is also a brilliant inventor and engineer. Some people believe that Ock has telepathic abilities outside just being able to control his metal arms.

WEAPONS AND GADGETS

Ock's mentally controlled mechanical arms have increased his strength, speed, agility and fighting skills to superhuman levels! And because they are controlled by an evil mastermind, their functions are limitless...

During an experiment there was a huge explosion, which caused the harness holding the arms to become *fused* with Otto's body. When he awoke he discovered he could control the arms with his *mind!*

The accident seriously damaged Octavius' personality, and the now 'mad' scientist adopted his *Doctor Octopus* alias and turned to a life of crime...

Doctor Octopus was responsible for bringing together a group of super villains to destroy the web-slinger. After escaping jail (after Spidey had placed him there!), Ock contacted every crook to have ever battled Spider-Man. Electro, Kraven, Mysterio, Sandman and Vulture all replied and together they were known as the **SINISTER SIX!**

A GUIDE TO DOC OCK'S MECHANICAL ARMS

The arms can move at 90 feet per second and can punch through reinforced concrete.

Ock controls his metal arms with his mind, even when they are not attached.

Each arm is made from reinforced titanium steel.

The end of each tentacle can rotate 360° degrees.

The sharp pincers can rotate like screwdrivers.

The tentacles are attached to a stainless steel harness that circles Ock's body.

Each tentacle has four electric motors that power their movements.

The metal is unaffected by fire and freezing cold temperatures.

The arms are six feet long, but can extend to 24 feet.

A memory chip is housed in each tentacle, so the arms can save Ock if he is knocked unconscious.

Even though the arms are artificial, Ock can still 'feel' things through them.

21

CONTINUED ON PAGE 25...

23

CONTINUED FROM PAGE 23.

THE DOCTOR'S SURGERY!

DOCTOR OCTOPUS HAS DEVISED SOME DASTARDLY DIFFICULT BRAINTEASERS TO TEST YOUR *MENTAL METTLE!* CAN YOU COMPLETE THEM ALL?

Being a super villain isn't all about brawn — you need brains too!

SOLE SYMBOL!

Look at the science symbols and see if you can spot the *only* one that does not have a matching pair.

AGAINST THE CLOCK!

Doc Ock has eight ticking time bombs! You must stop them from exploding by choosing the order in which they should be diffused! Start with the one which has the least amount of time left and end with the one that has the most!

A. 145.13
B. 109.55
C. 823.46
D. 945.09
E. 110.04
F. 57.46
G. 11.59
H. 1.43

WRITE THE CORRECT ORDER HERE

1= □ 2= □ 3= □ 4= □
5= □ 6= □ 7= □ 8= □

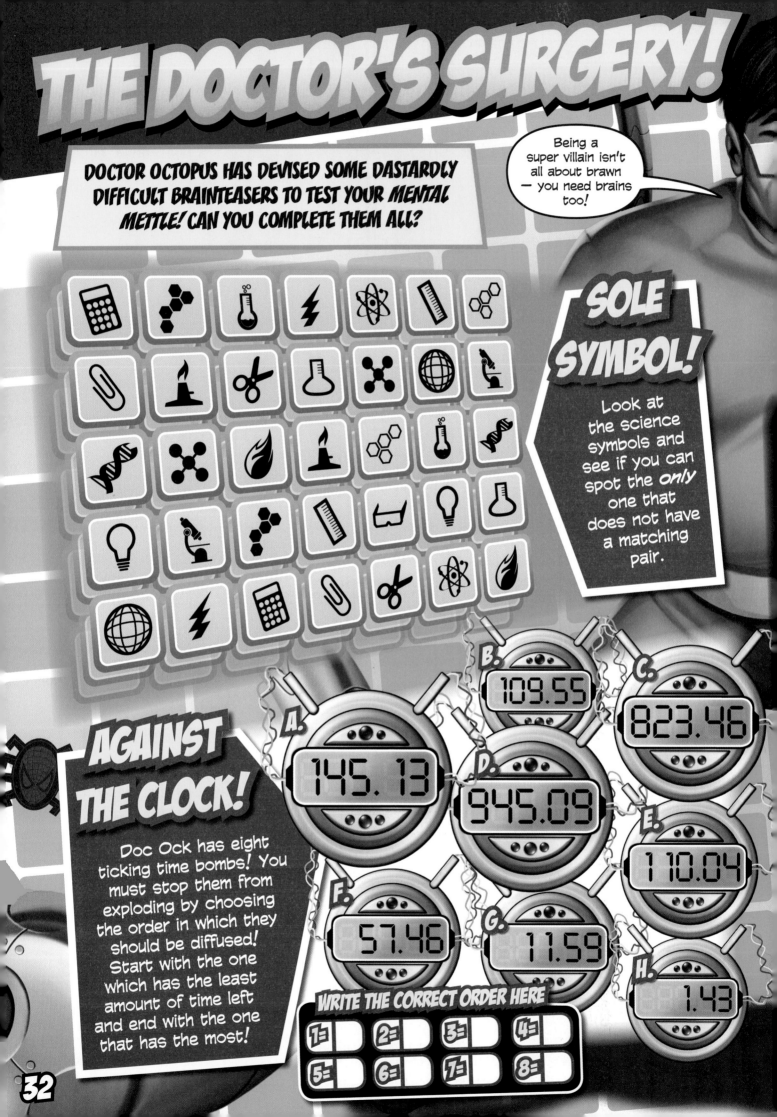

32

"HEY, GANG! IT'S TIME TO GRAB YOUR PENS AND PENCILS AND GET CREATIVE WITH YOUR FRIENDLY NEIGHBOURHOOD SPIDEY! SIMPLY ADD COLOUR TO ALL THESE COOL PICS, AND THEN WHEN YOU SEE AN EMPTY SPEECH BUBBLE - ADD SOME WITTY DIALOGUE!"

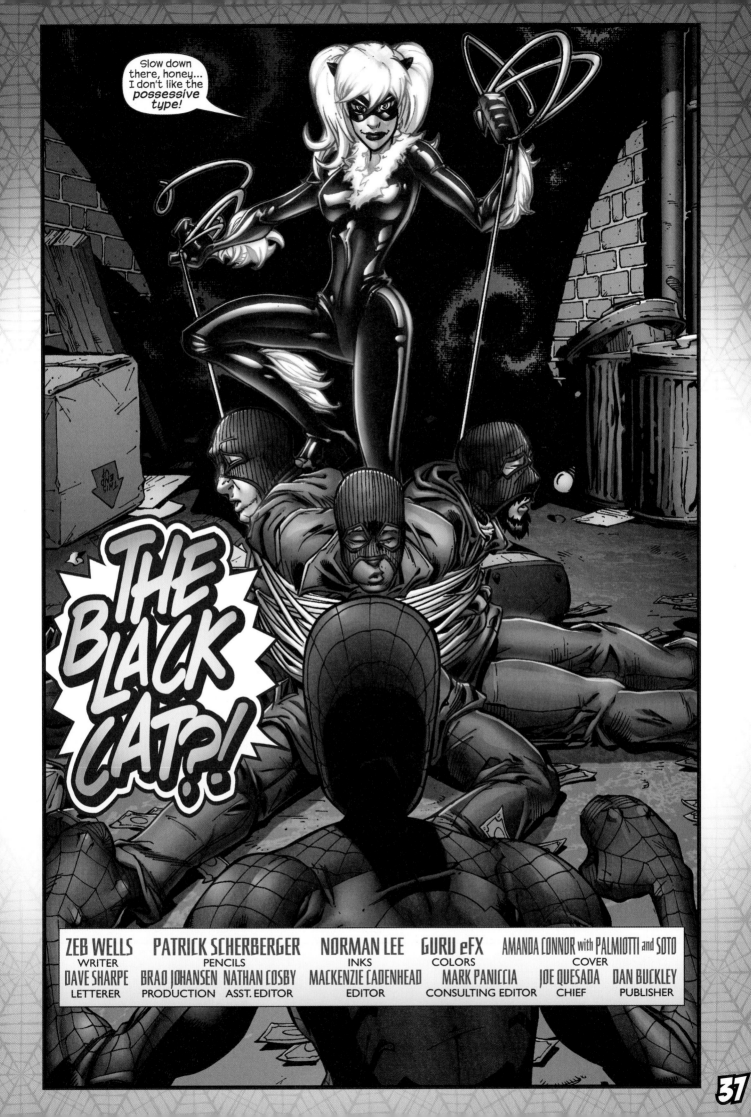

ZEB WELLS — WRITER
PATRICK SCHERBERGER — PENCILS
NORMAN LEE — INKS
GURU eFX — COLORS
AMANDA CONNOR with PALMIOTTI and SOTO — COVER
DAVE SHARPE — LETTERER
BRAD JOHANSEN — PRODUCTION
NATHAN COSBY — ASST. EDITOR
MACKENZIE CADENHEAD — EDITOR
MARK PANICCIA — CONSULTING EDITOR
JOE QUESADA — CHIEF
DAN BUCKLEY — PUBLISHER

42

CONTINUED ON PAGE 45...

BLACK CAT

DON'T BE FOOLED BY HER PRETTY FACE, THIS FEARSOME FELINE FELON IS AS COOL AND CONNIVING AS THEM COME...

After discovering her dad was a notorious cat burglar, a young Felicia Hardy decided to follow in his footsteps.

She learnt to pick locks and crack safes like a pro and then entered into an intense training regime, which transformed her into an expert gymnast and martial artist.

In the early part of her criminal career she used to tirelessly set *booby traps* near the location of her crimes, so when a would-be follower fell foul of one of her traps, it would give them the impression she had *luck* on her side!

Don't you know it's *bad luck* to cross the Black Cat?

CRIMINAL FILE #5318008

PERSONAL DETAILS

Real name: Felicia Hardy
Height: 5'10"
Weight: None of your business!
Eyes: Green.
Hometown: Queens, NYC.
Occupation: Cat burglar, adventurer and occasional crime fighter.

SKILLS AND ABILITIES

An eilte gymnast and martial artist, the Cat not only performs her tricks and flicks with style and finesse, she also packs a mean punch! Her most amazing ability, however, is to pass on 'bad luck' to her opponents.

WEAPONS AND GADGETS

Black Cat uses a super strong cable with a grappling hook attached to the end to either tightrope across or swing from building to building.

However, after some dodgy dealings with a major crime boss, called the *Kingpin*, she was granted the gift for real. The problem is she can't choose whom she gives misfortune to — now *anyone* who spends time with her is cursed with *bad luck!*

Despite their regular battles against one another, the Black Cat became attracted to Spidey and the two *even* began fighting crime *together*. But the Cat's new powers caused Spidey to become uncharacteristically *clumsy* and they were forced to end their relationship.

Whilst the break up hurt Felicia, she's not one to lick her wounds. Like most cats, she knows she'll *always* land on her feet...

CONTINUED FROM PAGE 43.

Later...

Spider-Man has proven his true colors by stealing a priceless artifact! The NYPD has promised to double their efforts and make Spider-Man public enemy number one!

BANK HEIST THWARTED BY FANTAS

Peter who? I'm sorry, but Liz is out on a date with Flash Thompson. He asked her to the spring formal tonight...and she said yes!

I'm sorry you "can't find" your homework, Mr. Parker. I'm afraid I'll have to give you a zero...

Just ran out of pasta! Don't worry though, got some leftover sloppy joe from Monday.

Last Monday.

"Black cats are only bad luck if they cross your path...or, I suppose, if you cross *them*...

"This "little guy" is an ancient Hawaiian idol. They say it's bad luck..."

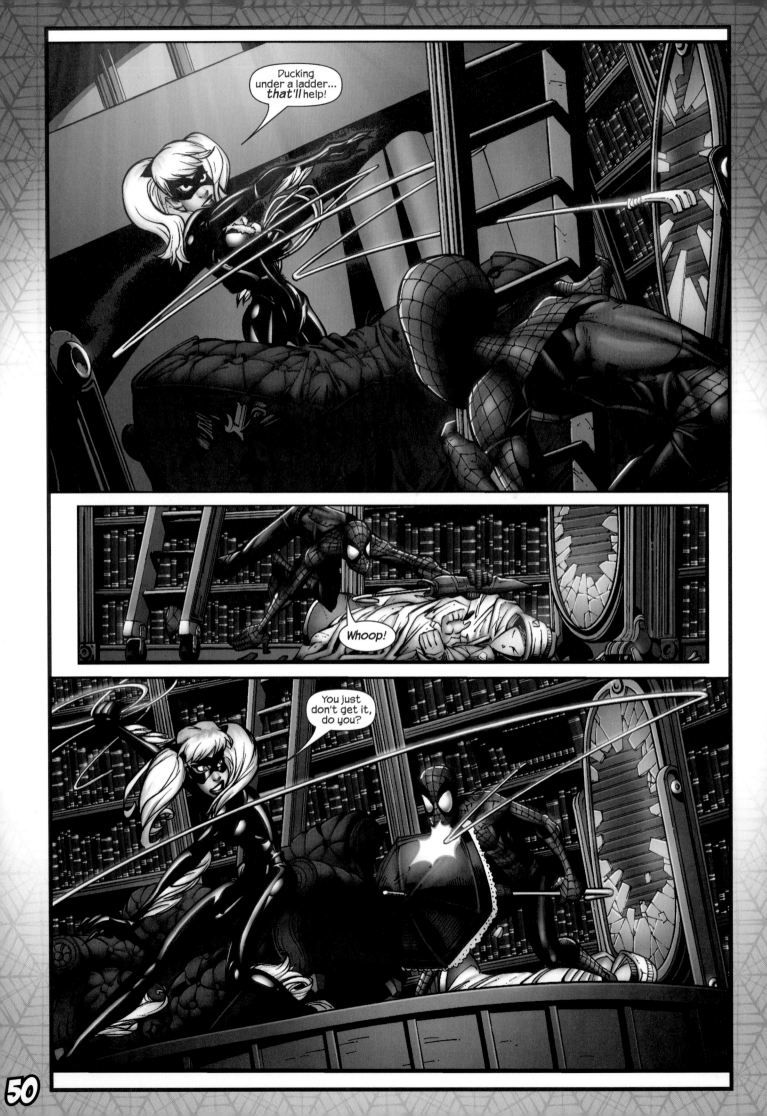

CONTINUED ON PAGE 53...

A WEEK IN THE LIFE OF... SPIDER-MAN

IF YOU THINK SPIDEY HAD A HARD TIME WITH THE BLACK CAT, YOU HAVEN'T SEEN ANYTHING YET. LOOK AT AN AVERAGE WEEK IN THE WEBBED WONDER'S LIFE AND YOU'LL SOON REALISE WHY HE IS FAMOUS FOR BEING UNLUCKY!

> Oh boy! This is gonna be expensive...!

MONDAY: I'm happily swinging around town when I run out of webbing and crash through a very expensive window! What a *smashing* start to the week!

> Get out of here you masked menace!!

> Yikes!!

TUESDAY: Feeling in a charitable mood, I offered to help out at a retirement home. Unfortunately for me, the ladies there believe *everything* J. Jonah Jameson writes in the paper!

> You won't like the Hulk when he's *hungry!*

> RRRR!

> Hee-hee-hee...

WEDNESDAY: When I popped over to see Iron Man, I didn't think he'd mind me helping myself to some pizza in the fridge... How was I supposed to know it belonged to the incredible Hulk?!!

THURSDAY: What could possibly go wrong at a kid's baseball game, I hear you say? Well, one thing's for certain I didn't count on my arch-rival, the *Green Goblin*, being one of the umpires!

FRIDAY: I thought I was being clever catching a free ride by clinging onto the underside of an aircraft. However, I didn't count on the plane belonging to the crazed super villain, *Doctor Doom!*

SATURDAY: Visiting the *Fantastic Four's* headquarters, I accidentally broke their security system, which meant the Super Heroes were locked in a small room for hours... needless to say, they weren't happy!

SUNDAY: My trip to the aquarium wasn't the fun-filled day I had expected, especially when the sea-dwelling psycho, *Orca*, and his pet whale tried to turn your friendly web-slinger into *fish food!*

ANSWERS!

Page 24
ORIGINAL OCK!

⑤

Page 5
AMAZING ANIMAL ABILITIES!

MAGNIFICENT MOLE-MAN

Ability to dig really big holes in double-quick time to trap thieves escaping on foot!

OUTSTANDING OCTOPUS-MAN

Can sucker punch up to eight super villains at any one time!

INCREDIBLE CRAB-MAN

Can inflict an extremely painful pinch, which causes felons to surrender!

BRILLIANT BED BUG-MAN

A villains' worst nightmare — he has the ability to catch crooks while they sleep!

SENSATIONAL SKUNK-MAN

Can create a super powerful stench, which causes criminals to fall unconscious!

Page 32
SOLE SYMBOL!

Page 32
AGAINST THE CLOCK!
WRITE THE CORRECT ORDER HERE

1= H 2= G 3= F 4= B
5= E 6= A 7= C 8= D

WORD NERD! Page 32

G D A Q I L
A S M R I W P O L S
A O M A P O
T Y B R S B R E O K Y
C E T U C P L M
B Y T E S B V E Y U N A
A V E O N R
A A E R V C A T E A A H A
A T C P

Page 33 CRACK THE CODE!

I WILL SQUASH
SPIDER-MAN
LIKE A BUG!

NINE LIVES!
Page 52

START!

FINISH!

Hey, web-heads! Did you spot all the spider symbols? They were on pages 5, 6, 24, 32, 33, 34, 35 and 60.